My Book of Favourite Rhymes

Kali Stileman

PICTURE CORGI

My Book of Favourite Rhymes

Little Bo-Peep

Little Bo-Peep has lost her sheep,
And doesn't know where to find them;
Leave them alone, and they'll come home,
Wagging their tails behind them.

Mary Had a Little Lamb

Mary had a little lamb,
Its fleece was white as snow;
And everywhere that Mary went,
The lamb was sure to go.

It followed her to school one day,
Which was against the rule;
It made the children laugh and play
To see a lamb at school.

Jack and Jill

Jack and Jill
Went up the hill,
To fetch a pail of water;
Jack fell down
And broke his crown,
And Jill came tumbling after.
Up Jack got, and home did trot,
As fast as he could caper.
He went to bed to rest his head,
With vinegar and brown paper.

Baa Baa Black Sheep

Baa, baa, black sheep,
Have you any wool?
Yes, sir, yes, sir,
Three bags full.
One for the master,
One for the dame,
And one for the little boy
Who lives down the lane.

Pat-a-Cake, Pat-a-Cake

Pat-a-cake, pat-a-cake, baker's man,
Bake me a cake as fast as you can;
Pat it and prick it and mark it with B,
And put it in the oven for Baby and me.

Sing a Song of Sixpence

Sing a song of sixpence,
A pocket full of rye;
Four and twenty blackbirds
Baked in a pie.

When the pie was opened,
The birds began to sing;
Wasn't that a dainty dish,
To set before the king?

Higgledy Piggledy

Higgledy Piggledy,
My black hen,
She lays eggs
For gentlemen;
Sometimes nine,
And sometimes ten,
Higgledy Piggledy,
My black hen!

Polly, Put the Kettle On

Polly, put the kettle on,
Polly, put the kettle on,
Polly, put the kettle on,
We'll all have tea.
Sukey, take it off again,
Sukey, take it off again,
Sukey, take it off again,
They've all gone away.

EGGS
FOR
SALE

Old King Cole

Old King Cole was a merry old soul
And a merry old soul was he;
He called for his pipe, and he called for his bowl
And he called for his fiddlers three.

Every fiddler, he had a fiddle,
And a very fine fiddle had he;
Oh there's none so rare, as can compare
With King Cole and his fiddlers three.

Hickory, Dickory, Dock

Hickory, dickory, dock,
The mouse ran up the clock.
The clock struck one,
The mouse ran down,
Hickory, dickory, dock.

The Queen of Hearts

The Queen of Hearts
She made some tarts,
All on a summer's day.
The Knave of Hearts
He stole those tarts,
And took them clean away.
The King of Hearts
Called for the tarts,
And beat the Knave full sore.
The Knave of Hearts
Brought back the tarts,
And vowed he'd steal no more.

Little Jack Horner

Little Jack Horner
Sat in the corner,
Eating a Christmas pie;
He put in his thumb,
And pulled out a plum,
And said,
"What a good boy am I!"

Ride a Cock Horse

Ride a cock horse to Banbury Cross
To see a fine lady upon a white horse.
With rings on her fingers and bells on her toes,
She shall have music wherever she goes.

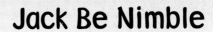

Jack Be Nimble

Jack be nimble,
Jack be quick,
Jack jump over
The candlestick.

Wee Willie Winkie

Wee Willie Winkie runs through the town,
Upstairs and downstairs in his nightgown,
Tapping at the window, crying at the lock,
"Are the children in their beds,
For it's past ten o'clock?"

Little Miss Muffet

Little Miss Muffet
Sat on a tuffet,
Eating her curds and whey;
Along came a spider,
Who sat down beside her
And frightened Miss Muffet away.

Round and Round the Garden

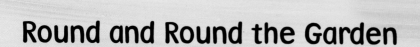

Round and round the garden
Like a teddy bear,
One step, two step,
Tickle you under there.

Incy Wincy Spider

Incy Wincy Spider climbed up the water spout.
Down came the rain, and washed the spider out.
Out came the sun, and dried up all the rain,
And Incy Wincy Spider climbed up the spout again.

Mary, Mary, Quite Contrary

Mary, Mary, quite contrary,
How does your garden grow?
With silver bells and cockle shells,
And pretty maids all in a row.

Donkey Riding

Were you ever in Quebec,
Stowing timbers on a deck?
Where's the king in his golden crown
Riding on a donkey?

Hey ho, and away we go,
Donkey riding, donkey riding,
Hey ho, and away we go,
Riding on a donkey.

This Little Piggy

This little piggy
Went to market.

This little piggy
Stayed at home.

This little piggy
Had roast beef.

This little piggy
Had none.

And this little piggy went,
"Wee! Wee! Wee!" all the way home.

Humpty Dumpty

Humpty Dumpty sat on a wall,
Humpty Dumpty had a great fall.
All the king's horses
And all the king's men
Couldn't put Humpty together again.

The Grand Old Duke of York

Oh, the grand old Duke of York,
He had ten thousand men;
He marched them up to the top of the hill,
And he marched them down again.

And when they were up, they were up,
And when they were down, they were down,
And when they were only half-way up,
They were neither up nor down.

There Was a Crooked Man

There was a crooked man,
And he walked a crooked mile.
He found a crooked sixpence
Upon a crooked stile.

He bought a crooked cat,
Which caught a crooked mouse,
And they all lived together
In a little crooked house.

There Was an Old Woman Who Lived in a Shoe

There was an old woman
Who lived in a shoe.
She had so many children
She didn't know what to do.
She gave them some broth
Without any bread.
She spanked them all soundly
And put them to bed.

One, Two, Three, Four, Five

One, two, three, four, five,
Once I caught a fish alive.
Six, seven, eight, nine, ten,
Then I let it go again!
Why did you let it go?
Because it bit my finger so!
Which finger did it bite?
This little finger on my right.

One Potato

One potato, two potato,
Three potato, four.
Five potato, six potato,
Seven potato, more!

Three Blind Mice

Three blind mice.
Three blind mice.
See how they run.
See how they run.

They all ran after the farmer's wife,
Who cut off their tails with a carving knife,
Did you ever see such a thing in your life,
As three blind mice?

Two Little Dickie Birds

Two little dickie birds, sitting on a wall;
One named Peter, one named Paul.
Fly away, Peter! Fly away, Paul!
Come back, Peter! Come back, Paul!

One, Two, Buckle my Shoe

One, two,
Buckle my shoe;

Three, four,
Knock at the door;

Five, six,
Pick up sticks;

Seven, eight,
Lay them straight;

Nine, ten,
A big fat hen!

One For Sorrow

 **1** for sorrow,

 **2** for joy,

 **3** for a girl,

 **4** for a boy,

 for silver, **6** for gold,

 **7** for a secret,
never to be told.

Hey Diddle Diddle

Hey diddle diddle,
The cat and the fiddle,
The cow jumped over the moon.
The little dog laughed
To see such fun,
And the dish ran away
With the spoon.

Other books by Kali Stileman:

★ Big Book of My World ★ Big Book of Nursery Rhymes
★ My Book of Songs and Lullabies ★ My Book of First Words
★ My Book of Numbers, Shapes and Colours
★ Peely Wally ★ Time for Tea, Polly Wally

PICTURE CORGI

UK | USA | Canada | Ireland | Australia India | New Zealand | South Africa

Picture Corgi is part of the Penguin Random House group of companies whose addresses can be found at
global.penguinrandomhouse.com.

www.penguin.co.uk   www.puffin.co.uk   www.ladybird.co.uk

Penguin
Random House
UK

First published in Great Britain as part of BIG BOOK OF NURSERY RHYMES by Doubleday in 2012
Published by Picture Corgi 2013
This edition published 2017

001

MIX
Paper from
responsible sources
FSC® C018179